BRYAN LEE O'MALLEY'S

edited by James Lucas Jones | design by Bryan Lee O'Malley & Keith Wood

Published by Fourth Estate

First published in 2004 in the United States by Oni Press.

First published in Great Britain in 2010 by
Fourth Estate
An imprint of HarperCollins*Publishers*
77–85 Fulham Palace Road
London W6 8JB
www.4thestate.co.uk

11

ISBN: 978-0-00-734047-7

Printed in Great Britain by Clays Ltd, St Ives plc

special thanks to
  Hope Larson
  Christopher Butcher
  Carla, Amanda, Catriona & Lynette
  James Lucas Jones
  AND YOU.

JUST SO I TELL YOU BEFORE YOU HEAR SOME DIRTY LIES FROM SOMEONE ELSE, YES, I'M DATING A 17-YEAR-OLD.

WALLACE WELLS
ROOMMATE
25 YEARS OLD
RATING: 7.5/10

IS HE CUTE?

HA, HA, HA, HA, HA.

I / can't be sure / but I think I heard you / crawl thru the door / you / didn't say a word / and i think you tried to go to bed
but instead you went to floor / you've been out drinking with the other boys again / telling them no we are only friends

Hey Kids! Now you can play along with Sex Bob-omb at home! It's easy, because they're kind of crappy! Look, this whole song only uses 3 chords!

G   C   Em

4/4 rock, fast, hard, sloppy

end / and where do you begin? / you've been out partying with guys i've never met / drinking beer and smoking cigarettes
killing brain cells and killing me / oh stop pretending / that this isn't really ending / and I will stop resenting you

RIIIING

RIIIING

SCOTT W. PILGRIM
Wallace P. Weldon
JUNK MAIL PLZ.

RIIIIIING

RIIIIIINGy

...HELLO?

SCOTT?
DID I WAKE
YOU UP?
IT'S TWELVE
THIRTY!!!!

STACEY PILGRIM
19 YEARS OLD
YOUNGER SISTER
RATING: "T" FOR TEEN

OHH... NO...
I'VE TOTALLY
BEEN AWAKE
FOR SEVERAL
HOURS.

SEVERAL.

YEAH,
RIGHT!
WHAT'S THIS
I HEAR
ABOUT YOU
DATING A
SIXTEEN-
YEAR
OLD?!?!

WHERE ARE WE GOING NOW? YOUR SECRET LAIR?

MY SECRET LAIR IS ONE OF THOSE "NO GIRLS ALLOWED" DEALS, ACTUALLY.

SO WHERE?

IT'S... OKAY, IT'S MY OLD HOUSE. IT'S WHERE I LIVED WHEN I WAS IN HIGH SCHOOL.

DO YOUR PARENTS STILL LIVE THERE?

NO, THEY LEFT... THEY SOLD IT. *SIGH*

SCOTT, I FORBID YOU FROM HITTING ON RAMONA, EVEN IF YOU *HAVEN'T* HAD A GIRLFRIEND IN OVER A YEAR.

DUDE, HE'S GOING OUT WITH A HIGH SCHOOLER RIGHT NOW. HIS MOURNING PERIOD IS OFFICIALLY OVER.

UGH... SCOTT, SHE'S TOO GOOD FOR YOU, OKAY? LET'S LEAVE IT AT THAT.

AND ANYWAY, I'M NOT EVEN SURE IF SHE REALLY DID HAVE A BIG BREAKUP.

SHE'S KIND OF VAGUE ABOUT IT, SO I HAD TO PIECE IT TOGETHER INTUITIVELY. SHE JUST KEEPS MENTIONING SOME GUY NAMED GIDEON...

I DON'T KNOW WHAT IT IS ABOUT THAT GIRL. SHE JUST--

FORGET ABOUT IT, SCOTT!

SO...

...I GOT US A SHOW.

OH YEAH?

WE IN THE INDUSTRY CALL THEM "GIGS", STEPHEN.

OH MY GOSH WHEN?!

IT'S ON WEDNESDAY AT THE ROCKIT. THIS GUY AT WORK WAS LIKE "STEVE, DO YOU KNOW ANYONE IN A BAND?", AND I WAS LIKE--

GREAT STORY, MAN.

WEDNESDAY NIGHT?? I'LL HAVE TO... I'M GONNA HAVE TO PULL SOME MAJOR TRICKS TO GET OUT OF MY HOUSE FOR THIS.

4

RAMONA COME CLOSER

I... I'M
NOT SURE
IF I...

24 HRS

LATER

MATTHEW PATEL WAS THE ONLY NON-WHITE, NON-JOCK KID IN SCHOOL. PROBABLY THE ONLY ONE FOR MILES AROUND, OR IN THE ENTIRE STATE, FOR ALL I KNOW. SO, OF COURSE...

KISSY KISSY

WE JOINED FORCES AND TOOK 'EM ALL OUT. WE WERE ONE HELL OF A TEAM. NOTHING COULD BEAT MATTHEW'S MYSTICAL POWERS COMBINED WITH MY BRUTE STRENGTH.

NOTHING BUT PRE-ADOLESCENT CAPRICIOUSNESS.

SORRY ABOUT THAT GUY. HOW MUCH DID HE LEAVE?

UMM...

AWW, MAN... $2.10?! THAT'S NOT EVEN ENOUGH FOR THE SUBWAY BACK HOME!

DUDE, I'LL LEND YOU THE FIFTEEN CENTS.

WICKED! LET'S GET OUT OF HERE BEFORE EVERYONE GETS REALLY MAD AT ME...

LATER ON

SO...

DO YOU WANNA... SORTA... GO OUT WITH ME?

YEAH, OKAY.

DO YOU WANNA MAKE OUT?

SURE.

NEXT!

Does Scott & Ramona's burgeoning relationship have a future? Isn't Scott still supposedly dating Knives Chau? Who is Ramona's second evil ex-boyfriend, and why is he in Toronto? Who are The Clash At Demonhead, and what kind of bizarre art-punky music do they play? Who's their hot girl keyboardist, and what's her relation to Scott? Why are they Knives Chau's new favorite band? Fights! Drama! Secrets revealed! The answers to all these questions and more! It's all coming in...

SCOTT PILGRIM VERSUS THE WORLD

BRYAN LEE O'MALLEY

LOVED BY ANIMALS

Illustration of the Author by Corey S. Lewis The Rey

BRYAN LEE O'MALLEY has been alive since 1979. He plays some guitar and keyboards, but is pretty bad at bass. His first book was called **LOST AT SEA**. His second book is this one. You can learn more about him at **WWW.RADIOMARU.COM**